ROSARIO + VAMPIRE

Season II

AKIHISA IKEDA

Tsukune Aono accidentally enrolls in Yokai Academy, a high school for monsters! After befriending the school's cutest girl, Moka Akashiya, he decides to stay...even though Yokai has a zero-tolerance policy toward humans (a fatal policy). Tsukune has to hide his true identity while fending off attacks by monster gangs. He survives with the help of his Newspaper Club friends— Moka, Kurumu, Yukari, and Mizore. But then his cousin Kyo comes to visit, and Tsukune can't keep the true nature of the school a secret from her when the Lilith Mirror reveals the true identity of whoever gazes into it!

The entire monstrous student body goes berserk, the school is destroyed, classes go on hiatus, and Tsukune returns to the human world. Until...

Tsukune Aono

Only his close friends know he's the lone human at Yokai and the only one who can pull off Moka's rosario. Due to repeated infusions of Moka's blood, he sometimes turns into a ghoul.

Moka Akashiya

The school beauty, adored by every boy. Transforms into a powerful vampire when the "rosario" around her neck is removed. Favorite food: Tsukune's blood! ♡

Kurumu Kurono

A succubus. Also adored by all the boys—for two obvious reasons. Fights with Moka over Tsukune.

Yukari Sendo

A mischievous witch. Much younger than the others. A genius who skipped several grades.

Mizore Shirayuki

A snow fairy who manipulates ice. She fell in love with Tsukune after reading his newspaper articles. ♡

Shizuka Nekonome

Tsukune and friends' homeroom teacher and News Club advisor. Loves fish. ♡

Ruby Tojo

Proud disciple of the late witch Lady Okata. Only learned to trust humans after meeting Tsukune. Now assist Yokai's headmaster.

Tenmei Mikogami

Yokai's mysterious headmaster, who saved Tsukune by giving him a Holy Lock to seal his ghoulish nature.

ROSARIO+VAMPIRE
Season II

Contents **1**

1: A Brand-New Season

Dear Tsukune...

How are you?

Tsukune Aono

Moka Akashiya

...is reopening this spring!

Yokai Academy...

I got some great news today!

GTNK

GTNK GTNK

HEH HEH... LETTER FROM A FRIEND, EH?

SWSH

!

And I can't wait to see you, Tsukune!

I can't wait for spring!

—Moka

I miss you a lot.

I can't believe it's been nearly half a year since they shut it down.

BRRRM

...BUT IT'S STILL THE SAME SCHOOL!

THEY FIXED UP THE YOKAI ACADEMY BUILDINGS...

...OR IT COULD COST YOU YOUR LIFE.

YOU BETTER KEEP YOUR GUARD UP...

?!

GWWHHHHHHH

PSSH

BRRRR

THIS IS THE ONLY PLACE I CAN BE WITH MY FRIENDS...

GTNK GTNK

BRRRM

RRM RMBR

RRMB

I'LL BE FINE. I'M COMING BACK WITH MY EYES WIDE-OPEN.

TA

...ALREADY HAS A LOVER—TSUKUNE AONO!

AND DON'T HIT ON HER!

MOKA...

JSH

HUH...?

MOKA?

RABBL RABBL

DON'T LET TSUKUNE HEAR YOU SAY THAT!

I KNOW. BUT THAT'LL KEEP THE HOUNDS AWAY.

HE'S NOT MY... "LOVER"!

?!
?!
?!

BRR BRR

YADA YADA

TEE HEE

OH, NOTHING! FORGET I MENTIONED IT!

HEAR WHAT?

TSUKUNE... DID YOU HEAR...?

WHAT?! THIS PUNY GUY?!

AND THAT'S THE AFORE-MENTIONED TSUKUNE.

Great timing!

TSU...

TSUKUNE?!!

BLSH SHF SHF Ahaha!

...

...SO... CUTE...

SHE'S...

I CAN'T LOOK STRAIGHT AT HER!

SHE'S TOO CUTE!

F WAPPA

AAAAH

AHH

HER SMILE MAKES IT ALL WORTHWHILE.

BUT... I'M SO GLAD I CAME BACK...

TATATA

HEY! TSUKUNE!

BUT OUR LOVE IS IMPOSSIBLE!

BE-CAUSE...

TMH

I GUESS... I REALLY DO LOVE HER...

PNG

WAAAGH!

IT'S BEEN TOO, TOO LONG!

HNNNN

K-KURUMU!

JUST TSU-KUNE'S GROUPIE.

KURUMU KURONO.

WHOA! WHO'S THAT?

"GROUPIE"?!

MWSH

I LOVE YOU!

I MISSED YOU SO MUCH!

....

KEEP YOUR DISTANCE, KURUMU.

AAAH!

SPLRT

TSUKUNE IS MY TURF.

WAAAGH

HWSH

KLING

SHHH

MIZORE!

NO FAIR! WHY IS THAT CLOWN SO POPULAR?!

MEET MIZORE SHIRAYUKI... TSUKUNE'S STALKER.

ANOTHER ONE! ALSO CUTE!

EEEK

YOU'LL HAVE TO READ SEASON ONE TO FIND OUT!

All ten volumes.

UM...

HOW LONG HAVE YOU BEEN IN THAT BUSH...?

IT'S BEEN A WHILE, TSUKUNE.

18

19

WOO

HOOT

KRMBL

...YAY

YOKAI ACADEMY'S MANDATE IS TO TEACH YOU HOW TO DO THAT.

Yokai

Coexistence

Review
Monsters

TP TP

Humans

Earth

Monsters who don't transform=Monsters

FOR US MONSTERS TO SURVIVE, WE MUST LEARN TO COEXIST WITH THEM.

THE EARTH IS RULED BY HUMANS...

...I'M THE LONE REAL HUMAN AT THIS SCHOOL FOR MONSTERS!

YEAH... BUT WHAT HARDLY ANYBODY HERE KNOWS IS...

GOT IT, TEACH!

SO DURING YOUR STUDIES AT YOKAI, YOU ARE REQUIRED TO SUSTAIN YOUR HUMAN GUISES AT ALL TIMES!

THE KEY TO CO-EXISTENCE IS TO ACT HUMAN!

...CAN NEVER BE!

AND THAT'S WHY OUR LOVE...

I can't wait to see you, Tsukune!

Moka

GWNG

I'M IN THE SAME CLASS AS TSUKUNE THIS YEAR!

YES! YES! YES! ♡

NNNNN

TOO MUCH DESTINY...

PLUS, WE'VE GOT MS. NEKONOME FOR HOMEROOM AGAIN.

ACTUALLY... WE'RE ALL IN THE SAME CLASS THIS YEAR.

IT MUST BE DESTINY!

...

PNG

OW OW OW OW!

HE MUST WANT US TO PROTECT YOU! WELL, LEAVE IT TO ME!

GRRP...

KRK

KRSH

ANYBODY ELSE SEE THE HEAD-MASTER'S HAND IN THIS...?

LOOKS LIKE EVERYBODY WHO KNOWS TSUKUNE'S TRUE IDENTITY IS IN THE SAME CLASS.

ZWRL

YEAH! I WONDER IF THEY CHANGED ANYTHING?

HEY, LET'S CHECK OUT ALL THE BUILDINGS THEY FIXED UP!

...

...? WAS MOKA STARING AT ME JUST NOW...?

RABL RABL

RABL

RABL

OOH, I HATE THIS!

EVER SINCE YUKARI CALLED US "LOVERS"...

...I'M TOO SELF-CONSCIOUS TO TALK TO TSUKUNE!

24

KISS
ME.

Y-YOU'RE
RIGHT...
I DON'T...
REALLY
FEEL...LIKE
MYSELF.

WHAT?!
RIGHT
NOW? OUT
THIS OF THE
ISN'T BLUE?!
LIKE YOU,
MOKA...

K-K-K...?

WHOA!

YAAAAAH!

NO... NOT ON THE HAND EITHER.

JUST... AN OLD-FASHIONED KISS?

O-OKAY. YOU MEAN LIKE...ON THE HAND, RIGHT?

GRRRG

MWAH

FVAP FVAP

NOT *THAT* KIND OF KISS.

ANYWAY... I DIDN'T MEAN ON THE *LIPS*.

HERE.

WHAT'S GOING ON?!

MOKA, YOU REALLY AREN'T YOURSELF TODAY!

GRR

ON THE THIGH ?!!

SPIRI

THIS IS EMBAR-RASSING!

I DON'T CARE! JUST HURRY!

WAAGH!

29

30

KURUMU!

GRRP

VWSSHH

Succubus

NEXT TIME YOU'RE FULL OF PASSION...

LISTEN, TSUKUNE...

HOW COULD YOU FALL FOR THAT CHEAP TRICK? YOU'VE GOT ME!

AND WHAT DO I FIND?!

I HAD A FUNNY FEELING SOMETHING WAS UP, SO I FOLLOWED YOU.

FWP FWP

NRRK

HUH?

WHAT?

38

YOU SEE, SHE'S VERY POWERFUL ALL THE TIME... BUT HER GOODY-TWO-SHOES PERSONALITY GETS IN THE WAY!

HER SHOW OF STRENGTH PROVES IT.

UH-HUH! I FREED MOKA FROM ALL HER INHIBITIONS!

DO YOU HAVE ANY IDEA WHAT YOU'VE DONE?!

A... LOVE POTION?

SHE WON'T HAVE ANY PROBLEM OVERPOWERING TSUKUNE NOW!

THIS IS 100 PERCENT RAW MOKA!

COME ON. WE'VE GOT TO STOP MOKA!

OKAY... I GET IT NOW.

WHICH IS ONE MORE STEP IN THE RIGHT DIRECTION FOR MOI AND TROIS!

TEE-HEE!

GO MOKA!

...THAT THIS IS ALL YOUR FAULT!

YUKARI, I TOTALLY UNDER-STAND...

41

42

43

44

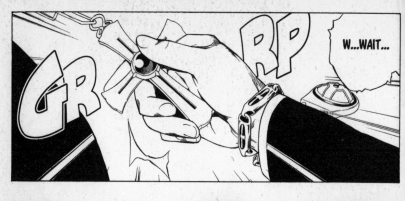

OH GREAT! SUDDENLY I DON'T KNOW MY OWN STRENGTH...

AAAAAAAHHH

FSSSS

ZSHW

...MOKA'S TRUE IDENTITY IS LOOSE.

AND NOW...

...SO IF IT'S REMOVED...

...MOKA'S TRUE NATURE...

AH...

THE ROSARIO SEALS MAGIC POWERS...

AH...

TA TA TA   TA TA   TA TA TA   TA

FSSHHH

...BECAUSE OF A LOVE POTION?

SO MOKA'S ONLY ACTING LIKE THIS...

!!

YUKARI SLIPPED MOKA A LOVE POTION?!

A...LOVE POTION?

THERE'S NO OTHER POSSIBLE REASON A HIGH BORN VAMPIRE LIKE ME...

...WOULD EVER WASTE TIME ON A WORM LIKE YOU!

Vampire

51

NEXT DAY...

...BUT I THINK I CAUSED YOU A LOT OF TROUBLE YESTERDAY.

I DON'T REALLY REMEMBER MUCH...

CLNK

I'M S-SORRY, TSUKUNE.

AHA HA!

DON'T BE MAD, OKAY?

UM...

AND HERE I THOUGHT SHE WAS FINALLY... ACTUALLY...

SIGH... SO SHE ONLY WANTED ME BECAUSE OF THAT LOVE POTION.

SNIF

SO I GUESS WHATEVER I DID...I REALLY WANTED TO DO.

ALL THAT LOVE POTION DOES IS DRAW OUT YOUR TRUE FEELINGS.

ACCORDING TO YUKARI...

EVERY SINGLE DAY...

...FOR THE WHOLE ENTIRE BREAK.

I REALLY DID MISS YOU, TSUKUNE!

HUH?

...WANT TO SUCK YOUR BLOOD SO BAD!

...I...

YOU MEAN... BECAUSE YOU...?

MOKA !!

M-HM

BECAUSE...

B-DM B-DM

B-DM B-DM B-DM

54

I LOVE YOUR BLOOD! ♡

SHMP

...WAS JUST ABOUT THIS?!

SLRP

SO ALL THAT STUFF THAT HAPPENED YESTERDAY...

SLRP

SLRP

M-MY BLOOD...?!

YOU'RE IMPOSSIBLE, MOKA!

I'M NOT FOOD!

SPLK

PLEASE SAY I CAN KEEP DRINKING IT! ♡

YOUR BLOOD IS SOOO TASTY!

THANKS!

SHIP

2: Self-Study Class

57

THE GREATEST GIFT I CAN GIVE YOU...

...ALL OF ME.

!!

PLRP

RRB

AFTER ALL...

AND IN RETURN...

...YOU'LL GIVE ME ALL OF YOU.

K-KURUMU...

58

59

60

...IS TO TEACH MONSTERS TO COEXIST WITH HUMANS.

...THE MISSION OF THIS SCHOOL...

AS YOU KNOW...

AHA

HA HA HA HA HA HA

WHICH MEANS MAINTAINING HIGH ACADEMIC STANDARDS.

IT'S ALSO ABOUT SUCCEEDING IN THE HUMAN WORLD.

BUT THAT DOESN'T MEAN MERELY PASSING AS HUMANS.

HYO

OOO

OKAY...

MOKA? CAN YOU SOLVE THIS?

ALL RIGHT. NEXT PROBLEM.

COMPLETELY HOPELESS...

...I MAKE A TOTAL FOOL OF MYSELF!

OH NO! I'M FINALLY IN THE SAME CLASS AS TSUKUNE AND...

It's okay.

Sure was a nice dream though.

SINCE LOG$_A$ 625=4 IS 625=A^4 ...

SWSH

625=25X25
=5X5X5X5
=5^4.
IN OTHER WORDS, A=5.

SWSH
SWSH

VERY GOOD.

IT FOLLOWS THAT A^1=5 WHICH IS A=5.

THEREFORE:
4 LOG$_A$ 5=4
LOG$_A$ 5=1.

OR, BY MAKING USE OF LOGARITHMIC FUNCTIONS:
LOG$_A$ 625=2LOG$_A$ 25
=2·2LOG$_A$ 5.

62

63

64

66

67

THAT'S THE ONLY REASON?!

WELL... BECAUSE THERE'S A LOT OF FRUIT IN SEASON!

And how is this educational?

WHY ARE WE... HUNTING... FRUIT?

EXCUSE ME, MS. NEKONOME...

F-FRUIT HUNT?!!

WE MUST TAKE ADVANTAGE OF NATURE'S BOUNTY!

KAW KAW KAW

FWP FWP

THIS FOREST IS FULL OF WILD STRAWBERRIES AND GRAPES...

AND SINCE BIRDS COME TO EAT THEM... IT'S ALSO FULL OF CARNIVOROUS PLANTS THAT FEED ON THE BIRDS!

UM.... DID YOU JUST SAY SOMETHING... REALLY SCARY?

...THE MONSTER DURIAN!

AND THIS IS THE PRIZE OF THE HUNT...

EWW!

GYA HAA

GAME ON!

BMM

THE MONSTER DURIAN HUNT...

THAT'S ALL!

I DON'T WANT ANYONE GETTING LOST EITHER— SO DON'T STRAY TOO FAR OFF THE PATH.

THIS FOREST IS DANGEROUS, SO REMAIN IN GROUPS OF FOUR OR MORE.

YAAAY

HMM... CAN'T REMEMBER...

WAIT... I THINK I'VE HEARD ABOUT THIS DURIAN SOMEWHERE...

73

74

75

NOW THE DURIAN... AND TSUKUNE.... BELONG TO—

LETTING HER PREY SLIP FROM HER GRASP...

MOKA IS A FOOL...

GHHH

THD
THD
THD
THD
THD

GAH!

YOU HIT *ME* TOO, YOU IDIOT!

HURRY!

AND JUST LEAVE THEM?!

SHF SHF

LET'S GO, TSUKUNE!

THE DURIAN GOT AWAY AGAIN!

IT'S ALMOST AS IF... IT'S MAINTAINING A CERTAIN DISTANCE FROM US!

WELL, IT RUNS IF WE CHASE IT...BUT WE NEVER LOSE SIGHT OF IT.

H-HOW SO...?

H-HEY... ISN'T THAT THING ACTING... A LITTLE STRANGE?

GHYUH HFF

HE

HE

...TRYING TO *LURE* US SOMEWHERE...

LIKE IT'S...

HM? YUKARI, IS SOMETHING WRONG? YOU LOOK SCARED...

...

GLANCE GLANCE

CAN KURUMU HANDLE THIS?

WE GOT SEPARATED.

COULD IT BE...?

I REMEMBER...

...SOMETHING ABOUT THIS DURIAN...

...MIGHT BE A LITTLE OUT OF OUR DEPTH HERE.

WE...

WE'LL NEED EVERYONE *TOGETHER* TO DEAL WITH THIS.

ARE YOU NUTS? VICTORY IS IN MY GRASP!

I'M NOT WAITING FOR *THEM* TO GRASP IT!

...

I DON'T THINK WE SHOULD TAKE THAT THING ON ALL BY OURSELVES.

LET'S WAIT FOR THE OTHERS HERE.

HUH ...?

WGL

WGWL WGWL

THAT'S NOT THE POINT!

...DON'T YOU WANT TO EAT THE DURIAN WITH ME?

BUT...

THIS IS NO TIME FOR IN-FIGHTING.

BUT I'VE GOT A BAD FEELING ABOUT THIS... WE NEED THE OTHERS.

GRRP

!!

TATA TA TATA

YOU'LL KEEP SLIPPING AWAY FROM ME.

IF I WAIT FOR THAT STUPID VAMPIRE...

...YOU'LL NEVER BE MINE.

Ge

Geh Geh

SEE? I CAN NAB IT ALL BY MYSELF!

K- KURUMU...

82

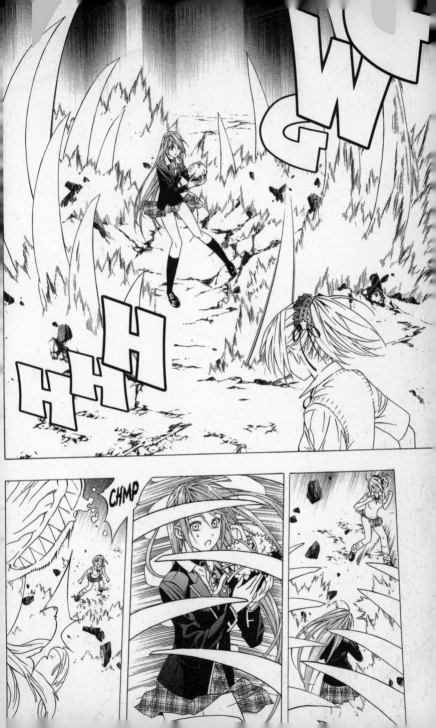

HOOOOOOO

MS. NEKO-NOME...?

SHOULD WE SEND IN THE CAVALRY?

THAT PESKY FRUIT AGAIN.

SOUNDS LIKE SOMEBODY GOT TRAPPED.

WELL, WELL...

HE HE HE HE

...THIS IS A *SELF-STUDY* CLASS!

AFTER ALL...

Got one!

THEY'LL LEARN A GREAT DEAL MORE BY SAVING THEM-SELVES.

BOB

BOB

OH... WE MUSTN'T CODDLE THEM.

HEHEH...

I GUESS THAT WAS THE IDEA...

ZSSSS

BUT DANGER COMES WITH THE TERRITORY!

SURE, STUDENTS GET HURT...

THIS CLASS IS SUPPOSED TO GIVE MONSTERS THE SKILLS TO SURVIVE IN A HARSH WORLD.

...WHEN THEY ADDED SELF-STUDY TO THE CURRICULUM.

I HOPE EVERYONE MAKES IT...THIS YEAR.

HEHEHE

MWCH MWCH

...

CHOP

SHLOOOP

IT SMELLS LIKE... BLOOD AND OLD SOCKS.

EEEEEEK

Sure is.

TWTCH TWTCH

AND SO SWEET! ♡

MWCH MWCH

SO RICH!

THIS DURIAN IS... DELICIOUS!

AND IT'S BEEN YEARS SINCE A STUDENT ACTUALLY BROUGHT BACK A DURIAN!

HE HE HE

ALL THE MAIN OBJECTIVES OF THE SELF-STUDY!

THIS CLASS DID WELL.

"BONDING WITH FRIENDS," CHECK.

"DECISION-MAKING SKILLS," CHECK.

I can't do it! I can't!

GAG

...ONLY TSUKUNE AND I WOULD BE EATING THIS TOGETHER.

MWCH MWCH

Y'KNOW, IF I'D GOTTEN MY WAY...

IT'S STILL NICE SHARING IT WITH ALL MY FRIENDS.

BUT I HAVE TO ADMIT...

REALLY NICE.

INDI-GESTION: ONE.

MINOR INJURIES: EIGHT. SERIOUS INJURIES: ZERO.

A FIRST FOR THE SELF-STUDY CLASS!

RABL RABL

TSUKUNE!

RABL

BLEAGH

CHMP

•••

N...NO... THAT'S OKAY...

COME ON! IT'S DEE-SCHMI-CIOUS!

UGH...

COME ON, TSUKUNE! HAVE SOME!

KURUMU...

BLUSH

3 : Superglue Girl

...AN ORDINARY HIGH SCHOOL SOPHOMORE.

TSUKUNE AONO...

...OOZING DROOL...

...AND CREEPING SLOWLY TOWARD ME.

IT'S CROUCHED DOWN LOW... GLARING AT ME...

THIS MIGHT SOUND KINDA WEIRD, BUT... AT THE MOMENT, I'M FACE-TO-FACE WITH A MONSTER.

IN OTHER WORDS... I'M SCREWED.

105

SHLP

OOOOH... I BET YOU TASTE SO-O-O GOOOOD!

?!!

WAAAAAGH

WHAT IS IT WITH MY BLOOD?!

YOU TOO?!

A REALLY, REALLY SCARY FRESHMAN...

SHE MUST BE A FRESHMAN...

RABBL RABBL

OH YEAH... FOR NEW STUDENTS.

THE WELCOME CEREMONY...?

GNG

THE WELCOME CEREMONY'S STARTING!

SHOOT!

OH!

GOTTA GO!

BONG BONG

110

MOKA?

TATA

AND A PET BAT?

KNEE-SOCKS?

YEAH, YEAH! IN FACT...YOU LOOK ALMOST TOO MUCH LIKE...

KIIII

YEAH! YEAH!

ANIME STYLE? LIKE THIS?

KINDA ORANGEY BROWN, YEAH...

DID SHE HAVE... LIGHT BROWN HAIR?

NO... WAY.

SSSSSH!

TMM

SSS

MOKA ?!!

114

116

'CAUSE FIGHTING IS FUN! ♥

BM

GK

BMM

KNK

G

HOW FAR BACK DO THEY GO...?!

MOKA!

BWH

LIKE OLD TIMES!

HIT ME WITH EVERYTHING YOU'VE GOT!

OH!

TA TA TA

117

OOPS.

DONNGG

BUH BUH BUH

KONG

UHH

WOW... THAT REALLY CONNECTED, HUH? YOU OKAY?

SORRY!

DRIP DRIP DRIP

DRIP

DRIP

· · ·

SHLUP

· · ·

GYAAA

TSUKUNE!

FUMP

AAA

118

SHE'S MY LITTLE SISTER!

YOU CAN'T HURT HER!

...SISTER?!!

YOUR...

SEE YA...

...BIG SIS!

...NEXT TIME...I'LL FORCE YOU TO TRANSFORM! AND WE'LL REALLY THROW DOWN!

THERE ARE TOO MANY PEOPLE AROUND RIGHT NOW, BUT...

120

YOU'VE GOT SOME EXPLAINING TO DO!

ENOUGH ALREADY, MOKA.

BLAH

BLAH

BLAH

BLAH

WE'VE GOT DIFFERENT MOTHERS, BUT WHEN WE WERE LITTLE, WE LIVED TOGETHER.

WE'RE THE YOUNGEST OF FOUR SISTERS.

HER NAME IS KOKO SHUZEN...

I NEVER LOST. NOT ONCE.

THIS WAS BEFORE MY POWERS GOT *SEALED* BY THIS ROSARIO, SO...

MY MEMORIES OF THAT TIME ARE KIND OF HAZY... BUT I DO REMEMBER WE FOUGHT *EVERY SINGLE DAY.*

122

TONS OF TIMES!

HAVEN'T YOU *TOLD* HER YOU CAN'T RELEASE THE SEAL ON YOUR OWN?

HER PERSISTENCE IS INSPIRING...

MHM

...SIBLING RIVALRY?!

WAIT A SEC... YOU MEAN THE ONLY REASON SHE ENROLLED HERE WAS...

HEY! THAT'S MY LITTLE SISTER YOU'RE TALKING ABOUT!

ANNOYING LITTLE PEST... WANT ME TO ENCASE HER IN ICE?

PWK

SHE THINKS IF SHE KEEPS PROVOKING ME, EVENTUALLY I'LL TRANSFORM AND FIGHT BACK.

BUT IT'S NO USE!

THIS MORNING SHE SAVED ME WHEN I WAS IN DANGER.

AHA HA HA

TSUKUNE...?

ARE YOU SURE BEATING YOU IS ALL SHE'S AFTER...?

I WONDER...

I WONDER IF THERE'S MORE TO THIS THAN JUST...

I THOUGHT SHE WAS REALLY NICE.

I'LL HANDLE KOKO ON MY OWN.

THIS IS BETWEEN US.

THANKS FOR YOUR CONCERN. BUT FORGET ABOUT IT.

127

KRMBL
KRMBL

WH... WHY...?!

...YOU WIN.

HUH?

I...I CAN'T GO ON, KOKO...

!!

I REALLY DID FIGHT MY HARDEST, BUT...

135

AND THIS AURA...

...LIKE MOKA'S... ALL DARK AND HUGE...

M-MOKA'S KICK WASN'T ENOUGH?!

R....

RRG....

RGH...

DDD...

DD...

D...

IT'S BEEN TOO LONG SINCE WE HAD A GOOD FIGHT.

I'LL PLAY WITH YOU AS LONG AS YOU WANT.

BRING IT ON, KOKO!

"MY... SISTER"?!

?!!

...

MY SISTER...

143

4 : Pride

A MONSTER RENOWNED FOR ITS GREAT POWER...AND OTHERWORLDLY BEAUTY.

THE VAMPIRE...

...MAKE HER THE PARAGON OF THIS SUPERIOR BREED.

THESE TRAITS SHINE BRIGHTEST IN ONE VAMPIRE IN PARTICULAR...

ONE WHOSE STRENGTH AND CHARACTER ...

MY DEAR SISTER...

146

BUT NOW ALL THAT REMAINS OF MY SISTER...

...IS THIS.

THANKS! ♥

CHMP

SHLRP

MY BIG SIS...

OOH! ♥ BUT YOUR BLOOD IS DELICIOUS ANYTIME!

ST-STOP! DON'T DRINK SO MUCH THIS EARLY IN THE MORNING!

HEY! MOKA!

WHAT COULD HAVE TURNED MY MOKA INTO THIS TRAVESTY?!

ALWAYS FAWNING OVER THAT WEAKLING TSUKUNE AND HIS BLOOD...

♥MORE!♥

NOT AN IOTA OF HER FORMER ELEGANCE AND POWER LEFT.

147

148

THE IDOL IN MY MIND JUST SHATTERED...

Like Toddlers!

SOB SOB

SCRE-E

BOP

BOP

BOP

ISN'T YOUR BRAIN STARTING TO ROT FROM HANGING OUT WITH THESE MORONS ALL THE TIME?

ALWAYS THE SAME ROUTINE, EH, TSU-KUNE?

MIZORE!

WMP

THUK

HWSH

THUK

ALL RIGHT! HERE SHE COMES!

YES! YES!

WHO YOU CALLING A MORON?!

...

YOU SHOW 'EM, SIS!

GRRRRRR

SPR!

THUK

NOW IF YOU WERE WITH ME, THE INTELLECTUAL STIMULATION ALONE—

YOU ARE SO PATHETIC! I HATE YOU!!

BOP BOP

AGH!! MOKA—

BOP

BOP

BOP

BOP

BOP

YOU'RE FAMILY. YOU SHOULD WORK THINGS OUT.

YOU STILL HAVEN'T MADE UP WITH YOUR SISTER?

KOKO?!

STUPID MOKA!!

HUH? KOKO! WHERE'D YOU COME FROM?

VWSH

BONG BONG

THOSE TWO ARE JUST TROUBLE.

FORGET 'EM, TSUKUNE.

YEAH, I KNOW... BUT...

150

THANKS TO YOUR AMAZING EFFORT LAST YEAR, WE'VE BEEN REWARDED WITH...

GREAT NEWS, EVERYONE!

News Club

LET'S USE OUR NEW HEADQUARTERS TO DO AN EVEN BETTER JOB THIS YEAR! ♡

...OUR VERY OWN CLUBROOM!

MEOW

SOUNDS LIKE THE SAME LOSERS SHE WAS HANGING OUT WITH THIS MORNING.

AND THOSE VOICES...

MY SISTER'S IN A "NEWS CLUB"?

SLNK

OKAY!

EXCUSE ME!

I'VE GOT TO GET HER AWAY FROM THEM! BY FORCE, IF THAT'S WHAT IT TAKES!

NOW I GET IT... IT'S THIS CLUB THAT'S RUINED HER!

YOU MEAN YOU CAN ATROPHY?!

SO... COMFY...

AHHH! YOU CAN REALLY KICK BACK IN A CLUBROOM...

HE HE

Y'KNOW, IF YOU CAN'T BEHAVE, YOU AND I ARE GONNA HAVE A PROBLEM.

NOW WHAT, KOKO?

WHAT?!

DON'T MAKE ME LAUGH, TWIN PEAKS!

I ALREADY DO—YOU.

PNG

A PROBLEM?! YOU WANNA KNOW YOUR PROBLEM?!

152

153

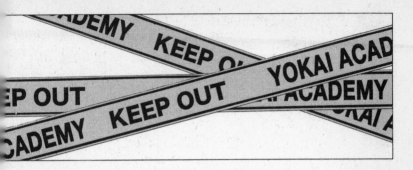

A PHANTOM ATTACKER!

STILL AT LARGE ON THE SCHOOL GROUNDS!

THERE ARE ALREADY TWELVE SERIOUS INJURIES AND THREE STUDENTS MISSING.

THEY SAY THE ATTACKER IS USING A KNIFE!

LOOK HERE! ALL OVER CAMPUS, STUDENTS ARE BEING ATTACKED TOTALLY OUT OF THE BLUE.

OR...IS HE FINISHING THEM OFF... SOMEWHERE ELSE?

IS THE ATTACKER KID-NAPPING THEM?

WHAT HAPPENED TO THE MISSING STUDENTS?

TWCH

IT'S CHAOS OUT THERE!

A KNIFE?! THAT'S... HORRIBLE!

KOKO?

GNNN

AAH!

OH, DREAM ON, MIZORE!

THIS IS A HOT STORY, ALL RIGHT. TSUKUNE—WANNA GO CHECK IT OUT WITH ME?

Tsukune's going with me!

AHAHAHA! I FEEL SO MUCH BETTER!

I FINALLY GOT YOU AWAY FROM THOSE BAD INFLUENCES!

YOU'RE TALKING ABOUT MY FRIENDS!

DON'T SAY THAT!

HANGING AROUND WITH LOSERS WILL TURN YOU INTO A LOSER!

YOU BETTER BE CAREFUL, MOKA.

KOKO!

HM...

SO THIS IS THE ENTRANCE TO THE UNDERGROUND DUNGEON, HUH?

IT IS PRETTY CREEPY...

...

FOR EXAMPLE... FINDING THIS PLACE.

!!

VAMPIRES LIKE US... WE LIVE IN A DIFFERENT WORLD!

LISTEN, SIS. THERE'S NO WAY YOU CAN BE FRIENDS WITH THEM!

C'MON, YOU HAD THAT *AHA* FACE TOO!

EASY TO FIGURE OUT... IF YOU THINK LIKE A *KILLER*.

IF YOU CONNECT ALL THE POSSIBLE ESCAPE ROUTES, THEY HAVE TO COME OUT... HERE.

AND HE'S GOT AN ESCAPE ROUTE.

THIS PHANTOM HASN'T BEEN COMMITTING THESE CRIMES AT RANDOM.

160

...WHAT?

THAT BAND OF SCOUNDRELS...?

Headmaster

!

GATHER ALL THE STUDENTS INSIDE THE SCHOOL!

THIS IS AN EMERGENCY.

SOMETHING THE MATTER, BOSS?

...TOOK A MISSTEP... AND APPARENTLY DECIDED TO HOLE UP HERE.

THEY WERE ON A RAMPAGE THROUGH THE HUMAN WORLD...

A GANG OF BANDITS HAS INFILTRATED THE ACADEMY GROUNDS.

Yokai Headmaster
Tenmei Mikogami

162

BATTY! WEAPON-IZE!

I GUESS IT'S TIME...

KU!

SHE'S PRAC-TICALLY GLOWING IN THE DARK! ♡

OOOH! LOOK AT HER FACE!

GULP

OH!

POOF

DM BDMP BDMP DM DM DM BDMP DM BDMP DM

S-SLAY HIM?! WITH THIS?!

IF WE DON'T SLAY HIM FIRST, HE'LL SLAY US!

C'MON! HURRY! I HEAR THE PHANTOM'S FOOT-STEPS!

YOUR WEAPON! HIT HIM! I'LL COVER YOU!

KOKO, WAIT! WHAT'S THAT...?

WHAT?!

HEAVY!

SHE TURNED RIGHT BACK INTO WIMPY GIRL!!

BUT THEN, THE SECOND SHE SAW YOU—

I ALMOST FINISHED LEADING HER BACK INTO THE DARKNESS!

YOU'RE *RUINING* MY SISTER!!

I KNEW IT! THIS IS ALL YOUR FAULT!!

I USED TO BE SO PROUD OF HER...

AS POWERFUL AS HER. AS BEAUTIFUL AS HER.

ALL I EVER WANTED WAS TO BE LIKE HER.

I *LOVED* HER.

KOKO... STOP THAT...!

!!

167

W-WHAT JUST HAPPENED? I KNOW MY GUARD WAS DOWN, BUT HOW COULD A *GIANT* LIKE THAT GET *SO CLOSE* WITHOUT ME NOTICING?

AND...

HUH ...?

TSUKUNE!

CLK CLK

NH...

ME, A VAMPIRE...

...SAVED BY A WORMY LITTLE DRIP LIKE HIM.

...HE SAVED ME.

FFFF

HUH ...?

KOKO!

BEHIND YOU...!

NOT WORTHY OF MY OWN FANGS.

I'M PA-THETIC.

IT'S ALL OVER.

SLU

PMUUU

170

SO THAT SOMEDAY, WE CAN DEFEAT YOUR SISTER.

WE'VE BEEN TRAINING HARD FOR MONTHS...

WHO YOU CALLING WEAK?

KIND OF LIKE IN A SHONEN MANGA...

WE CALL IT TRAINING OUR OWN "INNER MOKA." IT'S BEEN FUN.

IF YOU GO ON THINKING VAMPIRES ARE THE ONLY TOUGH MONSTERS...

...YOU'RE SETTING YOURSELF UP FOR A FALL.

WHILE YOU WERE STRIKING TOUGH-GAL POSES, I GUESS.

WHAT? N-NO! WHEN DID THIS HAPPEN?!

SAVE IT. TSUKUNE AND MOKA AREN'T HERE. DID THEY GET CAUGHT?

OH WELL... IF THEY'RE COMING THIS WAY...

WE'LL JUST HAVE TO KILL 'EM WHEN THEY GET HERE.

HEH HEH HEH

IT'S BECAUSE YOU GUYS WENT BERSERK.

I DIDN'T THINK THEY'D GET BY US SO QUICK.

HMM... IT'S GETTING NOISY UPSTAIRS.

...I RE-SPECTED THEM.

FOR ONE BRIEF SHINING MOMENT...

Sigh

IS NOT! IT'S YOUR FAULT!

POK

POK POK

THIS IS ALL YOUR FAULT.

MONSTER FRUIT [The End]

THE RIGHT WAY!

HOW TO SPEND YOUR BREAK

ROSARIO + VAMPIRE

Season II

Meaningless End-of-Volume Theater

This occurs during the break between seasons I and II.

I

• Kurumu and Mizore's Break 2 •

WAIT A SEC.

HEY!

HOOOOOO

SO SINCE WE'VE ALL BEEN OUT FOR PART OF THE SECOND SEMESTER...

YEAH. SO?

MIZORE, YOU WERE STUCK AT HOME THE WHOLE FIRST SEMESTER, RIGHT?

...YOU MIGHT NOT PASS THIS GRADE!

I'LL BE A FRESHMAN AGAIN NEXT YEAR?!

YOU MEAN...

• Kurumu and Mizore's Break 1 •

BORED.

YEAH.

THERE'S NOTHING TO DO OVER THE BREAK.

DITTO. IT'S EASIER TO JUST STAY AT SCHOOL.

I CAN'T VISIT TSUKUNE, AND IF I HANG AROUND AT HOME, MY MOM YELLS AT ME TO GO OUT AND PLAY...

MAYBE WE'LL GET A LITTLE SMARTER!

SHOULD WE GET SOME STUDYING DONE?

AND THAT'S HOW WE DECIDED TO TRAIN OUR "INNER MOKA."

WE'RE JUST MAKING EACH OTHER DUMBER.

WHAT ELSE IS THERE TO DO?

FORGET IT...

HOPELESS

Rosario+Vampire
Akihisa Ikeda

• Staff •
Makoto Saito
Kenji Tashiro
Nobuyuki Hayashi

• Help •
Takafumi Okubo
Naoya Suganuma
Tsuyoshi Nakamura
Hajime Maeda
Hirotaka Inoue
Yuta Nakagawa

• 3DCG •
Takaharu Yoshizawa

• Editing •
Makoto Watanabe

• Comic •
Kenju Noro

BE SURE
TO READ
VOLUME 2!
KIII!

IT'S MY JOB...

...TO PROTECT THE STUDENT BODY!

WE'VE GOT TO SAVE TSUKUNE AND MOKA!

THEY RUSH TO SAVE THEIR IMPERILED FRIENDS...

BUT ALL WHO LAY EYES ON...

DON'T GET TRICKED!

NO!

...HIS TRUE NATURE WILL DIE!!

AKIHISA IKEDA

I still haven't gotten used to calling this manga "Rosa-Vam." Who decides on these nicknames anyway? But it seems like it's "official," so I guess I'd better start using it too.

Thanks to all of you, Rosa-Vam is in its second season! The "II" means it's a continuation from "I," obviously... but it's totally fine to start with Season II. So please, start reading! From wherever you like! Whether you're new or returning, I hope you enjoy this story about Tsukune, Moka and their friends!

Akihisa Ikeda was born in 1976 in Miyazaki. He debuted as a mangaka with the four-volume magical warrior fantasy series *Kiruto* in 2002, which was serialized in *Monthly Shonen Jump*. *Rosario+Vampire* debuted in *Monthly Shonen Jump* in March of 2004 and is continuing in the magazine *Jump Square (Jump SQ)* as *Rosario+Vampire: Season II*. In Japan, *Rosario+Vampire* is also available as a drama CD. In 2008, the story was first released as an anime. Season II is also available as an anime now. And in Japan, there is a Nintendo DS game based on the series.

Ikeda has been a huge fan of vampires and monsters since he was a little kid. He says one of the perks of being a manga artist is being able to go for walks during the day when everybody else is stuck in the office.

ROSARIO+VAMPIRE: Season II
1
SHONEN JUMP ADVANCED Manga Edition

STORY & ART BY AKIHISA IKEDA

Translation/Kaori Inoue
English Adaptation/Gerard Jones
Touch-up Art & Lettering/Stephen Dutro
Cover & Interior Design/Hidemi Sahara
Editor/Annette Roman

VP, Production/Alvin Lu
VP, Sales & Product Marketing/Gonzalo Ferreyra
VP, Creative/Linda Espinosa
Publisher/Hyoe Narita

Printed in the U.S.A.

Published by VIZ Media, LLC
P.O. Box 77010
San Francisco, CA 94107

10 9 8 7 6 5 4 3 2 1
First printing, April 2010

www.viz.com

www.shonenjump.com

CRYPT SHEET FOR
ROSARIO+VAMPIRE: SEASON II, VOL. 2
MAGICAL CANDY

WHEN CONSUMING MAGICAL CANDY THAT MAKES
YOU INSTANTLY GROW OLDER, BEWARE OF...

a. emotional maturity

b. instantly growing younger

c. lumbago

Find out the answer in the next volume,
available AUGUST 2010!

SEE INTO THE SOUL
OF *BLEACH*
WITH THE MANGA,
PROFILES, AND ART BOOKS

Tell us what you think about SHONEN JUMP manga!

Our survey is now available online.

o to: **www.SHONENJUMP.com/mangasurvey**

Help us make our product offering better!

SAVE 50% OFF THE COVER PRICE!

IT'S LIKE GETTING 6 ISSUES FREE!

OVER 350+ PAGES PER ISSUE

THE WORLD'S MOST POPULAR MANGA

MAY 2010

This monthly magazine contains 7 of the coolest manga available in the U.S., PLUS anime news, and info about video & card games, toys AND more!

❏ **I want 12 HUGE issues of SHONEN JUMP for only $29.95*!**

NAME

ADDRESS

CITY/STATE/ZIP

EMAIL ADDRESS   **DATE OF BIRTH**

❏ YES, send me via email information, advertising, offers, and promotions related to VIZ Media, SHONEN JUMP, and/or their business partners.

❏ **CHECK ENCLOSED** (payable to SHONEN JUMP)   ❏ **BILL ME LATER**

❏ **CREDIT CARD:** ❏ **Visa** ❏ **Mastercard**

ACCOUNT NUMBER   **EXP. DATE**

SIGNATURE

CLIP&MAIL TO:

SHONEN JUMP Subscriptions Service Dept.
P.O. Box 515
Mount Morris, IL 61054-0515

P9GNC1

* Canada price: $41.95 USD, including GST, HST, and QST. US/CAN orders only. Allow 6-8 weeks for delivery.
ONE PIECE © 1997 by Eiichiro Oda/SHUEISHA Inc. BLEACH © 2001 by Tite Kubo/SHUEISHA Inc.
NARUTO © 1999 by Masashi Kishimoto/SHUEISHA Inc.

RATED
TEEN
ratings.viz.com

VIZ mEDIA
www.viz.com